THE BEST OF

MATT

1996

MATTHEW PRITCHETT studied at St Martin's School of Art in London and first saw himself published in the *New Statesman* during one of its rare lapses from high seriousness. He has been *The Daily Telegraph's* front-page pocket cartoonist since 1988. In 1995 he was the winner of the Cartoon Art Trust Award and was Cartoonist of the Year in 1992 and 1996.

The Daily Telegraph

THE BEST OF

MATT

1996

ORION

Orion Books
A Division of the Orion Publishing Group Ltd
Orion House
5 Upper St Martin's Lane
London WC2H 9EA

First published by Orion Books 1996

A CIP catalogue record for this book is available
from the British Library

ISBN 0 75280 625 4

Printed and bound in Great Britain by
The Guernsey Press Co. Ltd, Guernsey, Channel Islands

THE BEST OF

'YOU, yes _YOU_, Mr Robins,
may have already _WON_ the
chance of _NOT_ receiving
ANY junk mail during the
POST STRIKE!!!!!!!!!!!!!'

Political gleanings

'I've voted myself
an enormous tip'

'It's from me!'

MPs give themselves a huge pat on the wallet

Political gleanings

As the debate goes on about minimum wages and fat cats

Political gleanings

'No, it's STAKEholder'

'Oh make your mind up –
am I Old Grandma, or
New Grandma, New Danger?'

New Labour ...?

Political gleanings

'I should have put something more substantial than Labour's tax plans down the back of my trousers'

'I used to be a Labour front-bencher but I wouldn't take a vow of silence'

Blair gets tough on kids and colleagues

Political gleanings

'By the way, this doesn't affect my very strict views on law and order'

'We're proud to say a large number of leading hypocrites send their children here'

Harriet Harman sends her son to a grammar school

Political gleanings

'Remember to vacate your room by noon on the day of your defection'

But Blair isn't the only one with problems as Tory turncoats blackmail Major

Political gleanings

The Tories' privatisation campaign meets
the people

Political gleanings

Government criticises late payers

And the divorce bill
causes controversy

Political gleanings

"The King feels that there should be an element of 'fault' in divorce"

'We want one of those old-fashioned acrimonious divorces'

Political gleanings

'I'm going to be spending more time with my butler'

Political gleanings

Humphrey returns to
Number Ten

Blair gets tough with rebels

Political gleanings

Share issue makes instant loss

'I'm taking back the letters I delivered'

On off postal service for the summer

Education matters

'I'm going to get my husband to do mine'

'We mustn't draw too many conclusions from one set of figures'

Schoolgirl marries holiday lover as SATS are introduced to English schools

Education matters

'Write a story on how
number 8 feels about
having 3 subtracted from it'

'I found out why he's so
much brighter than his
friends - he's been
playing truant'

As teachers come under attack for their methods
once more

Euro 96

'In the event of the England team being on board, the parachutes are located . . .'

'I'll be Gascoigne, you be Sheringham and our jumpers can be the pub'

England kick off Euro 96 with drunken riot care of Cathay Pacific

Euro 96

And carry on the celebrations with a shock win over Holland

Euro 96

'And make sure nobody slopes off early to watch the football'

'So, . . . er . . . did anyone see the tennis?'

Setting up a grudge match against the old enemy

Euro 96

'Don't mention the match...'

More sporting moments

'Put on the replay of the
Bruno, Tyson fight – I want
to time my boiled egg'

Bruno comes to a
predictable end

'You'd better test him as well'

And the testing begins before
the Olympiad's opening races

More sporting moments

'Sometimes it goes for as long as ten minutes without showing any sport'

The marathon continues from Wembley via Wimbledon to Atlanta

More sporting moments

'I really think the
English can win this'

'I'm just popping out to
do a spot of rioting'

Euro 96 nationalism transfers to tennis with a
surprise British showing

More sporting moments

'Play is suspended for 25 years until global warming gives us the same climate as the Loire Valley'

As usual play occasionally interrupts the rain at Wimbledon

More sporting moments

'It always takes me a few days
to get my gin and tonic legs'

'The lads were hoping
you'd let Shearer out
for a kick-around'

Newcastle Utd buy Shearer for
£15 million

Royalty in trouble again

Diana reveals all - including her bulimia - on
prime time tv prompting critics to take sides

Royalty in trouble again

Pleas from the Queen for a quickie divorce

Royalty in trouble again

'We don't talk any more'

The country is fascinated as Di has another
change of heart about those close to her

Royalty in trouble again

'Was it part of the
divorce settlement
Your Royal Highness ?'

'My wife has already
decided what to call me
after our divorce'

Fergie and Diana negotiate terms of settlement

Royalty in trouble again

'They can remove my toenail right away, but there's a six month waiting list if I want Princess Diana to be there'

'DON'T JUMP!'

Despite the splits there's no end to media interest

Royalty in trouble again

If it's not a love interest it's the state of their bank balances

The British beef crisis

'What's the scare of the day?'

The British beef crisis

'Bad news. Your Yorkshire
puddings are mad'

'How nutty is the cutlet?'

The British beef crisis

'Before I buy this steak
I want to know who
its parents were'

'You were supposed to
bring the export licences'

European reaction brings about
beef war

The British beef crisis

'There'll be mad cows over the white cliffs of Dover . .'

The British beef crisis

'Hey! Somebody's
been hiding pieces
of beef in here'

'I've got a pen friend in
Europe – and once a month
I refuse to write to her'

Foreign leaders treated to traditional Sunday
roast as non-co-operation starts

The British beef crisis

Euro public enemy no. 1

'You're looking good, Ariane'

Ariane Euro rocket blows up on lift off

The British beef crisis

'Phew, if my sister hadn't told me about Mad Chocolate, I might have eaten that Easter egg'

And eventually the sheep takes the rap

Lottery fever

'We have visited planet
Earth and brought back
14 million lottery tickets'

'Scratch away the surface
to reveal three Cezannes
and win £50,000'

Syndicates take a fancy to rollover numbers

Lottery fever

'The next hymn will be. . . number 17'

'Oh no, it's the vicar – quick, hide the lottery tickets'

Church takes exception to mammoth wins

Lottery fever

'I had to do it - she had the same three winning lottery numbers as us'

'What happens if an unusually large number of other people also find the Holy Grail?'

Camelot admits there may not be enough cash for £10 winners

Lottery fever

'What would be going through my mind at this point?'

'It's a £14m grant from the National Lottery'

Grants handed out

Law and order

Police under threat as numbers drop and they
find themselves on the wrong side of the law

Law and order

'I sentence you to prison for as long as it takes you to break out'

'I'd better go – I told my wife 266 days ago that I was on the OJ Simpson jury'

Old lags and celebrity suspects both get out of jail free

The Hello file

'I can never remember the names of Elizabeth Taylor's seven husbands'

'The silly names are coming five minutes apart'

The Hello file

'I'll have to charge you
£1,500,000 for that because
it used to belong to JFK'

Jackie O's trinkets make millions

Sting's sums don't add up as
accountant steals away

The Hello file

'Oh no, it's
Jarvis Cocker Spaniel'

Vogue attracts critics as Pulp star crits the BRITS

The water crisis

'Three bluebottles to see
you, Mr Newton'

Water chief advocates fewer baths in time
of shortage

The water crisis

'This isn't a rain dance – it's a compensation dance'

Incensed customers demand compensation for leaky mains

The water crisis

'We have a wide selection of waters for you to choose from'

Quality criticised as water companies compete for trade

Global warming

'COME OUT, I know you're in there!'

... brings unseasonal extremes

Global warming

'Apparently, by 2025, Fergie and Diana could be holidaying in North Yorkshire'

... at home and abroad

Getting about

'You can tell the age of a
road scheme by the number
of protesters in the tree'

The Newbury bypass stops traffic ...

Getting about

'There goes the neighbourhood'

'I was abandoned as a baby and brought up by by-pass protesters'

Getting about

... as Railtrack encourages its staff to ease overcrowding in the run-up to the sell off

Getting about

'QUICK, I want to sell my Railtrack shares, NOW!'

'Now I'm looking for someone with a curvy bit'

Getting about

'The good news is that the train is on time, the bad news is that it left 15 minutes ago'

Getting about

And it's no safer at sea as ferry runs aground off Calais

Our friends overseas

'I told my wife I was working late at the office and she reported me to the EC'

'I see you haven't quite got the hang of kilos yet'

European union means new rules at home and at work

Our friends overseas

'Shall I throw back the small notes?'

'So, gentlemen, the new Euro coin will be gold on the outside and delicious milk chocolate on the inside'

Our friends overseas

'And this is a
bonsai apology'

'Welcome to Iraqi
Election Night Special'

Demands for Japanese apology
on VJ day

Our friends overseas

'Old habits die hard for Nelson Mandela'

Mandela, the elder statesman, has trouble at home and new friends overseas

The state of the nation's health

'Is it for casseroling
or transplanting?'

'Wow! look, a hospital bed'

Pig organ transplants may become more
common than beds in NHS future

The state of the nation's health

'It's the only way I can be sure of keeping the bed'

And press causes furore over pregnant prisoners chained for childbirth

Green stuff

'Apparently, if you hold it up to your ear it blows your head off'

The French continue nuclear testing

'I'm building 4.4 million houses on the green belt'

And green belt is eroded

Green stuff

Another oil spill on UK coast

But the industry fights back

Art and the media

Arts controversy continues from traditional
problems to Damien Hirst's new wave

Art and the media

'This is the
BBC World Service'

'We think daytime TV is
stupid, so we video it and
watch it in the evening'

Reith's grand ambition overrun by daytime soap

Art and the media

'I can't get the
stupid *!*#**
V-chip to work'

'Good evening . . . bong . . .
shocked pupil taught to speak
by Trevor McDonald . . . bong
and finally, where's my supper?'

In-set censor invented as traditionalists fight
low standards

Miscellaneous

IRA drop ceasefire as talks founder

Miscellaneous

'OK, men, I want you to build a crude shelter and then the MoD will sell it'

'It's OK, men, it's one of ours'

MOD housing sell off planned ... as RAF gets cash boost from government

Miscellaneous

'It's hard enough being black, but if they find out I'm gay...'

'Fruitcake, vicar? Oh no, I shouldn't ask'

Establishment figures come out of the closet

Miscellaneous

'Our electric toaster has just beaten my husband at draughts'

Miscellaneous

'I spent all my money on
flowers and then my wife
ran off with the florist'

'Well, you're healthy
enough to be president
of Russia'

Miscellaneous

'I dreamt Charles and Diana got back together to make a record and it outsold the Beatles'

Beatles bring out a 'new' record

'Dad, Dad, will you take us to visit the stench at Kew Gardens?'

Flower opens after 33 years and it stinks of rotting flesh!

Miscellaneous

Cricketing libel case sees costs of £500,000
awarded against Botham and Lamb